ARE PIRATES POLITE?

ARE PIRATES POLITE?

BY **CORINNE DEMAS** & **ARTEMIS ROEHRIG**

ILLUSTRATED BY **DAVID CATROW**

SCHOLASTIC INC.

For Morgan, Devon, Ariadne, and Demetria —C. D. & A. R.

To my shipmates, Beetle, Blu, and Stubbie —D.C.

PIRATES are unruly

and pirates love to fight,

but pirates still say "please" and "thanks"

'cause pirates are polite.

Pirates shout outside on deck
while counting pirate gold,

but use their "inside voices"

when they're meeting in the hold.

Pirates plunder lots of ships
but don't forget their duty.

They always call out "thank you"
for all their stolen booty.

Sharing is what pirates do

when they find any treasure.

To make sure shares are equal,

their parrots help them measure.

Pirates' parrots can't be stopped

from parroting and squawking,

but pirates never interrupt

when another pirate's talking.

Pirates like their privacy

when doing something private,

so they knock on doors and don't barge in

on any other pirate.

Pirates think you're weird
if you've washed your face or hair,
but they always show respect
and never point or stare.

While pirates are in battle,

to push ahead is fine.

But when it's time to board the boat,
pirates wait in line.

When pirates dine at dinner
they're never, ever rude.

Even scallywags keep mouths shut

while they chew their food.

When pirates feast on chowder,
they try hard not to slurp,

and they always say "excuse me"

every time they burp.

If a pirate bumps another,

"I'm sorry," he will say,

instead of "You rapscallion!

Get thee from my way!"

Pirates love to duel

with swordplay of all sorts,

but at the end they say "good fight"

'cause pirates are good sports.

PIRATE MANNERS:

1. SAY "PLEASE."
2. USE YOUR INSIDE VOICE.
3. SAY "THANK YOU."
4. SHARE.
5. DON'T INTERRUPT.
6. KNOCK BEFORE YOU ENTER.

7. SHOW RESPECT.
8. WAIT IN LINE.
9. EAT WITH YOUR MOUTH SHUT.
10. SAY "EXCUSE ME."
11. SAY "I'M SORRY."
12. BE A GOOD SPORT.